"I've known Patrici... ...years and she has a very kind, forgiving, and loving spirit. The people or characters in *The Roses Are Too Perfect* seem so real and are established as they are brought into existence while skillfully revealing Trisha's complicated feelings and experiences. Subsequently, the character sees the gentle radiance come back into her life. This comes from the depths of Patricia's heart. Also, the story is very heartwarming and touching. I know you will enjoy reading it."

Connie Jones
Secretary, First Assembly of God Church,
Tucson, Arizona

"I have known Patricia for many years and she writes from her heart; a loving heart that anyone would understand. Her book is a true treasure."

Kenneth Kruger
Chairman, All American Airlines, Inc.

"Patricia is the most caring and innocent person I have ever met. *The Roses Are Too Perfect* took me into an innocent place that shines throughout the entire book. This book is as pleasant as Patricia is herself, and I think that anyone who has lost someone they hold dearly can truly benefit from this book."

Melissa Lynn Luksa
Office Manager, Norman Tag Agency
Norman, Oklahoma

THE ROSES ARE
too perfect

Patricia L. Cromwell

THE ROSES ARE
too perfect

TATE PUBLISHING & *Enterprises*

Published by Tate Publishing & Enterprises, LLC
127 E. Trade Center Terrace | Mustang, Oklahoma 73064 USA
1.888.361.9473 | www.tatepublishing.com

Tate Publishing is committed to excellence in the publishing industry. The company reflects the philosophy established by the founders, based on Psalm 68:11,
"The Lord gave the word and great was the company of those who published it."

Book design copyright © 2008 by Tate Publishing, LLC. All rights reserved.
Cover and Interior design by Stefanie Rooney

Published in the United States of America

ISBN: 978-1-60604-688-3
1. Fiction, Religious
2. Family & Relationships, Death, Grief, Bereavement
09.04.02

DEDICATION

I dedicate this book to my husband, John; without his constant encouragement, I would not have completed this book. I also dedicate this book to my children, grandchildren, brother, brothers-in-law, sisters-in-law, nieces, nephews, other family members, and friends who supported me in word and in deed throughout this endeavor. I pray it will touch lives in a positive, blessed way.

> The Lord will give strength unto His people;
> the Lord will bless His people with peace.
>
> Psalm 29:11 (KJV)

ACKNOWLEDGEMENT

I am so grateful that I was brought up in the small village of Tamms, Illinois, located in the very southern tip end of the state, eighteen miles north-west of Cairo, Illinois. Population 550, and for the most part, *good people*. This book's whereabouts is taken from my hometown of Tamms. Even though this presentation is fictional, much of this writing is contributed to my sweet memories of home, my folks and people from Tamms.

I wanted to acknowledge each individual by name that influenced my life, such as the members of my country church two miles down the road in Sandusky, Illinois; also friends, neighbors, and my family; however, I cannot. Attempting to do that would be too much to add.

I am so *proud* to have been a part of this community with its wholesome values and to have been reared in this place. It has been so beneficial to me.

I want to *Thank God* for making all of this possible, for without him, I am nothing.

TABLE OF CONTENTS

FOREWORD

This book has been an inspiration to me. I have recently lost two loved ones, and I know life continues. The heartache death leaves behind sometimes is hard to get past, but there is a place that can be found in Jesus Christ.

Life can and will get back to normal when you find that place that is special to you.

It is an honor to know Patricia Cromwell. Patricia has a beautiful gift from God that has been displayed through her writings.

I pray that you will enjoy this book as I have, and the words will help you find healing in whatever you may be going through.

Kathryn Jordan,
Women's Ministry Director
Heaven Bound PCG

LOVING THE
memories

As I, *Trisha Gleaton,* stood gazing at the shabby small piece of land, I recalled the legendary garden of roses that Mother once planted when I was a child. I could even see a few scraggly brushes here and there, peering among the dried-out weeds and overgrown grass. Oh yes, there is a small red one and her favorite, dark pink. They are so small. Although I had been gone for nine years, not caring for the roses at all, somehow they struggled to survive.

I left my hometown soon after Mother passed away. I couldn't bear the thought of staying around, feeling her presence, and not seeing her being active in her usual snappy way. It hurt too much. We were so close.

I remember Sundays of years gone by when my husband, daughters, and I would come over for Sunday dinner. Mother loved cooking for her family. She always fixed such wonderful, big dinners. She had kept up Dad's vegetable garden, and it was full of great things. She had string beans, corn on the cob, tomatoes, new potatoes, peas. I could go on and on.

When Dad was still with us, my husband, David, loved nothing more than to walk into Mom and Dad's house and grab the salt shaker. Then Dad would say with a great big grin on his little round face, "I know where you're headed." He was right too. David was going straight to the huge, red, juicy tree tomatoes to help himself! The corn was fourteen feet high by July fourth. Everyone loved to look and drive by slowly. When Mother didn't have fresh vegetables, she would can all that she could for winter. We were treated to the best warm peach cobbler in the world on dark, drizzly, cool evenings. Mom served it with a spoon of vanilla ice cream to top it off. It was so good that I don't have words to describe it.

I would help with the dishes, as she didn't have a dishwasher in those days. Mother washed and I always dried the fragile blue and cream colored stoneware cups, saucers, and plates. Mother never liked to dry them. She would use any excuse to let them drain and not have to pick up the dishtowel herself. She liked to soak pans overnight sometimes. She didn't like to scrub anything either. Mother said it was much easier to wash them after the food was loosened up a bit. I didn't mind the little task, but my feet were tired when we were finished. I do believe Mother used every dish she had in her cabinets when she prepared a meal. The twins liked to get involved and help out but were too small to be a real help. It seemed like it was more disastrous than not if we let the two-year-old girls join us.

While Grandmama and I were busy cleaning up the kitchen, Grandpapa and Daddy were good at getting Mitzi and Marie's attention. They took them outdoors to investigate the woodpecker holes and watch the chickens scratch and eat the feed that was thrown over or through the fence. The girls loved putting their little hands into the big bucket of corn and grain that Grandpapa would bring out for them to feed the baby chicks. Half or more of their handfuls would spill on the ground, but it didn't matter. The birds would get what the chickens didn't!

⤫

Dad passed on before Mother. Mother had her flowers, but Daddy had his vegetable garden. Mom lived alone, and she seemed to be happy most of the time. She missed Dad, so she had good days and bad days. Mother was a go-getter and didn't believe in feeling sorry for herself. When she felt sad, she would soon perk up and get herself busy. She didn't have a lot of money, but Mother was a good manager.

I never felt poor as I was growing up. My parents worked hard and believed if you put enough of yourself into a place, everyone would feel your love when they entered your home. Dad worked at the lumberyard, and Mom was always busy at home or church. I learned valuable lessons from my parents. They taught me that being rich didn't necessarily mean having a lot of money. One day, Mom told me that a rich person could still be a "pitiful, poor human being." Oh, how I miss Mama. She was such a dear person.

❧

The lawyers called me a month ago to come home and sign the papers. I couldn't bring myself to come until now. The place looked run down. Mom's heart would have been broken to see her lovely little dream house and all her trees in such bad condition. It looked like no one had lived here for years. I had so many loving memories of my mother, father, and this place.

My appointment with Mr. Cox was at two p.m. I was early, so I decided to drive by the house. I could not make myself open the front door. I just stared at the place and looked upon an old crumbling-down shack and weed-covered lot. I would have never recognized the place if I hadn't known where I was sitting.

❧

When I arrived at the courthouse, Mr. Cox greeted me with a smile and a warm cup of coffee.

"Mrs. Gleaton, you know that the little homestead will have to be sold for the taxes owed against it if you don't settle up. Also, there's the issue of what's owed on the last tenant's bill. Have you considered making up the difference and paying the taxes?"

I calmly said, "Yes, I will pay all that is due."

Mr. Cox was delighted; my decision would save him lots of nasty work, and besides that, he was fond of our family and remembered how the place had looked in its prime.

As for me, I wondered why I said yes and then remembered the roses. If I couldn't make myself go into the little house, the least I could do was clean up the lot and tend to Mother's lovely roses. That would be a start.

෧

The legal work was done, and I called David to see if he wanted to bring the girls down to help me clean up the place. I wasn't sure if they could turn loose of their busy schedules. Actually, I doubted they would come. I shocked my dear husband so badly that he nearly dropped his cell phone in a puddle of water. He caught it just in time, so there was no harm done!

"You haven't been back to Clayton in nine years, and you want to stay and clean up the little old dump? It doesn't make a bit of sense to me, but I miss you. The girls and I will be there in a couple hours, or I mean I'll ask the girls if they can make it. I'll buy a bucket of chicken on the way."

☙

Three hours or so had passed when my family arrived. Melissa (Mitzi) and Marie, the twins, jumped out of the van. They surprised me. Mitzi was a legal assistant and Marie was still in medical school. Both girls were yelling about how they had to throw some clothes into their luggage, makeup, and saying goodbye to boyfriends—you know, the works! David came straight to me, wrapping his arms tightly around me. He knew what a hard trial this had been and that I had succeeded!

"David, I decided that I don't want to rent out the place again after we fix it up. I don't know what to do just yet, but it is ours—lock, stock, and barrel."

"Well, Trisha, we don't have to decide what to do right away. We don't need to make a rushed decision. I won't even ask what you have in mind at all." I thought it was very nice of my husband of twenty-eight years to be so patient with me. He had always been the calm, easy-going type, and the Lord knows I needed just that!

❧

When I was a young girl, my mother said to me, "Trisha, the roses are too perfect. Winter will be here soon." I didn't pay much attention to it at the time, but as sure as the perfect rose bloomed, winter would not be far off. The prettiest rose bloomed the year Mother passed away. It was a dark pink rose. I had never seen the dark pink rose bloom as large and glorious with every petal as perfect as this one happened to be. Roses bloom in the springtime, different times in the summer and fall. A rose is a hardy, stout plant.

❧

We lived in southern Illinois. Mother taught me

about flowers. She had several different kinds, but the rose, well, I don't have words to relate the beauty and sweet fragrance. They hadn't bred the smell out of her flowers. The fence was lined with Seven Sisters roses. They were light pink, almost white, and each long stem produced seven little roses. When they were in full bloom, the large crawling vine covered the entire fence in the front yard. The sycamore and sassafras trees shaded the vines. No one could paint the picture I saw when I looked out from the front porch of our little cottage as I took in the fragrance of all the roses. When the roses were blooming, Mr. McCrite would drive down the road slowly, going to his little farm a couple miles south of our place. I know that he was smelling those wonderful blossoms as he passed on by. I loved thinking about the roses. What lovely memories.

MUCH *to do*

David was his own boss. He owned a successful computer service business. When he took time off, it was his own. He had dependable, loyal employees, which took a load off of him.

I had taken time out as I was a freelance writer and had finally gotten to the place where I could pick and chose my personal availability.

Now, it was a different story for our daughters. Mitzi had a week or so coming to her, and Marie only had two days off from school. We decided to continue to stay in the small Clayton Inn where we had a little kitchenette. It would work for the short time I had intended on being there. The room also had two queen beds, so Dad and I could have one and the girls the other. David and I had a comfortable old mattress, but it smelled a little musty, like the rest of the town. Marie would drive the van back and return the next weekend to get us. *That will work,* I thought.

෴

We all hugged Marie and said goodbye as we walked over to the flower garden site. *Much work to do* was all I could think of. Trellises were broken. Mother had various types of lovely lattice work. She even had an archway blanketed with climbing roses at the entrance of her little wonderland of flowers. It may sound as if it were, but it really wasn't overdone.

Since David's work kept him inside much of the time, he was looking forward to the exercise of walking the two miles back to Mr. Heater's Feed, Grain, and Hardware Store, where he would purchase the tools that he needed to start this unbelievable home improvement project. I stayed behind trying to pull up the weeds by hand. Some came up fairly easy because of the rain the week before, and others were tougher. Mitzi Renée sort of helped.

She kept me company telling me of many memories she had with Grandmama and Grandpapa. It made the time pass, and she really didn't want to mess up her manicure. She was such a fussy thing. Everything had to be just right, and dirt under her nails was not appealing to this dainty girl. Mitzi did help some, though. She would gather up the weeds I pulled and put them in a neatly-stacked pile. After a little while of this, she remembered that she had a lot of questions for Mr. Cox and wanted to visit him. I considered the fact that she could gain knowledge and would not be standing and staring at me, making me nervous, besides talking my ear off, so I told her to see if the old bike we found out back had good tires. It didn't. She proceeded to walk on up to Mr. Cox's office. He would probably enjoy talking to her. She told me she would see Dad and me at the inn. I had to remember that our little princess was all grown up now.

Mitzi was so inquisitive and full of questions for Mr. Cox. He had been a great friend to my parents. He didn't want our place to just be swallowed up by taxes and let any old bunch who desired move onto it, completing the final destruction of the place. Mr. Cox knew the background of the Scarbrough Cottage and the beautiful gardens. My dad, Roy Scarbrough, and Orville Cox were like brothers when they were young. They went hunting together, so he had a lot of old tales to tell my Mitzi, besides answering her most curious legal questions and putting her mind at ease. He told her of how her great grandmother had left this place to her grandpapa. A tear trickled down her soft cheek as she recalled the two tender faces of her grandpapa and grandmamma. They were special to her. She would never forget the warm, loving feeling each time she had a memory of either one of them. Grandpapa's mother, Grammie, had been the one to start the flower garden, and Grandmama had carried on the work and care of the Scarbrough Gardens. This made Mitzi feel proud. Remembering her grandparents meant the smell of moth balls, cedar, and all the good smells when Grandmama and Grandpapa would send a special package to her and her sister, just because. When she and Marie opened that little special something, both of them would say, "That smells like Grandmama's house."

Then the girls would just laugh. One would say, "Isn't that funny?" Their grandparents didn't need a specific reason to send a box or package to them because Grandmama and Grandpapa knew how they loved getting things in the mail with their own names on it.

The sweet memories also gave Mitzi somewhat of an incentive to help her dad and me a little more on the place. She thought that she might live there one day, although she didn't inform me of this thought at the time. Mitzi had been my quiet child when she was small, but when she got into the mix of things as she matured, she learned to be a real "jabber jaws" at times. She still kept a lot of things inside. Marie was the opposite. She could not help but spill the beans, no matter what!

౿

The week passed quickly, and most of our work was done. The little rose bushes that had peered up through all the weeds and overgrown grass were now fully exposed to the sunshine. They even looked happier, livelier. David had painted and repaired all of Mom's trellises and lattices. Now the shriveled-up little plants could stretch and grow up and out once again. The flowers could take in the sun and drink in all the rain. I knew they would flourish.

David had gotten the rose food and mulched, raked, watered, and redone all the flowerbeds. Many iris, tulip, and different kinds of bulbs were set back into the nice soil where they should be; they would sleep through the winter and wake in the spring, around Easter time. This was my mother's favorite time of year. I think it was my dad's too. One year he had somehow acquired a large pole, similar to a telephone pole. Dad had planted a climbing lilac that hung down the whole length of the pole. I can just picture it: green vines, leaves, and lavender (wisteria-like) blooms floating down from the top to midway on the pole. It wasn't far from the front door. When we walked out on Easter morning, ready for church, the fragrance rushed into your whole being. It was so delightful, just indescribable.

⟡

The week was gone, and Marie had returned. She was in a particularly good mood. She popped out and said, "Say, Mom and Dad, did you realize that it's only twenty days until Thanksgiving?"

"No" was all I could manage to say. In an instant, millions of memories flooded my mind as I heard my daughter say Thanksgiving. Mom's last Thanksgiving had been the best I could remember.

Marie was going on about how she had more time off from school and we could stay longer. One of David's employees had told her to tell her dad that the business was fine and to take off all the time he needed. I, for one, was ready to leave. If we stayed, the house would be next on the agenda. There was no way we could fix it in just a week or even a month. The repairs would take ages, or at least months.

Marie whined over and over as I explained the actual situation that confronted us. Marie was pushing me to the limit. She knew what buttons to push too. She loved to irritate me. I could never understand her reason for this behavior, but what could I do?

"Oh, no, I can't. I can't," I kept repeating. "Marie, give me a break! Get real!" I snapped back.

We decided that we would stay for a couple

days and seek out a contractor to refurbish the home, which would be done later. It would be getting cold soon, and no one would be able to work on a building in freezing weather.

We drove down to the house one last time before going back home. Still, I could not enter the house. The girls and David went in. I could hear one of my girls say, "I remember this. Grandmama always used to," and then I would plug my ears. Oh, how it hurt so. I sat on the porch swing, drying my eyes every few minutes. I got up and just stared at Mom's garden, searching out anything that needed touching up. At least I found solace there.

I could not believe how a week of nurturing could make such a difference. The roses were already changing. The bushes were looking stronger, and then I spotted one rose bush, "The Bush." The dark pink one had a small bud nearly fully open, and it looked like a picture in a magazine.

That rose is too perfect. Winter will be here soon, I thought.

CURIOSITY MADE *me do it*

The girls were always puzzled about the reason I couldn't bear going back into Mother's little house after she passed away. They felt closer to her when they touched her things and told me that they could still smell the slight scent of Grandmama's sweet perfumed hankies. They found comfort in this experience. I only wished I could bring myself to do that. We had kept some of her personal items locked up in a cubby. When the girls caught sight of the small room, they used their key to open it and sort through everything. I did wonder how things looked, but my heart felt like it was being ripped from my chest when I thought too long on Mother. I felt like a coward or whatever you call a woman who won't accept reality.

I had left the details about the house to Mr. Cox when Mother left us and he rented it out until things had gotten so run down. A few pieces of Mom's furniture remained in the cottage. He had tried his best to get me to come down sooner to examine the place, but I couldn't force myself to face the music. I understood what he had meant when I arrived. It was almost beyond repair.

Even though Mr. Cox did have his practice in this small place, he was only available part-time. His official office was located in Crankston, which was about forty miles away. Crankston was fairly large compared to Clayton. We always admired his work. He remembered his roots and came back to help those who couldn't get his kind of help any other way.

$\mathcal{C}$

After three weeks of this suffering, yet joyful experience, and many mixed emotions, I decided that my home back in Tunis needed me. I had asked my cousin, Peggy, to get my mail while we were gone and look after a few things for us at home. I knew she would be getting tired of doing that by now.

She had a low tolerance when it came to doing extra jobs for other people at times; at least that was my excuse to my family. She really wasn't that way at all. David and I went on home with the girls and checked out things. All was running smoothly, and Peggy was happy to see us come home too.

❧

Thanksgiving was growing near. Mitzi and Marie wished that the little place down in Clayton was all fixed up. It needed so many repairs. The roof needed to be replaced. Actually, the entire home needed to be gutted and rebuilt from the ground up. Exterminators had to come, broken windows fixed, etc. The list would go on and on. Besides that, I didn't know when I would be able to even think about literally going into that sweet house again. Stepping onto the porch and sitting in Mom's swing while I was there was a real trial.

When I was a teenager, Mom and I would drink our morning coffee on the front porch as we listened to the birds sing and feel the breeze. Yes, I was a normal teen, but some precious moments were had from time to time with my mother. And at that time, I didn't realize just how precious those memories would be to me until now. Even though I sat on that porch swing, it was still hard for me to even look at the place where I sat, shelled the peas, and laughed with Mama. I did revere that place, though. I didn't know what I was trying to do. Supervise? I couldn't even supervise myself, let alone anyone else. I believe I was talking "faith" to my inner being. If I could build myself up into really believing that I could do this project on the little cottage, then I could, right? David and the girls would help out on the supervising too.

Thanksgiving came and went. It was good, but the empty feeling would never leave me. My last Thanksgiving with Mother would forever be in my heart and mind. Her little house was small, but the totally secure feeling and warmth were irreplaceable. It felt roomy, even when it was crowded. Aunts, uncles, cousins came with their specialties in covered dishes. The little stone fireplace Dad had made in the center of the front room was always flickering and brightly burning when we arrived at noon. Four o' clock in the afternoon was the time Mom liked to have everyone gather around for the "Thanksgiving Prayer." Believe you me, we thanked God for every blessing Dad could recall, right down to the chicken feed he was able to buy from Mr. Heater. Sometimes, Uncle Ned would have to add a thing or two. By 4:45 p.m., our plates were full and overflowing. However, before all of that would happen, Mother made sure the three little widow ladies in our neighborhood had a good hot dinner. It was usually my job to carry their plates to their homes and personally hand them warm meals and greetings for the day. They always appreciated it so much. Mother was a giver, that's for sure.

Mom was always the last one to take her seat. She wanted to make sure everyone had what they wanted, and just in case they needed one more thing, she was "Johnny-on-the-spot!" No one would leave hungry from her house!

At last, after making sure everyone was served and satisfied, Mother would take her place at the table. Once again we would hear her say, "Hey, hey, my eyes were bigger than my stomach!" That was because she had sampled everything she cooked before it was to be given to anyone else, and she was already full before she sat down.

We would laugh because we were all as guilty as she was, grabbing little bits of turkey, so everyone held their hands over their mouths so they didn't lose what they had just put in. The children giggled and spilled their soft drinks or cherry Kool Aid, the popular drink for kids at that time. I watched Auntie Jane grumble as she sopped up the wet spots, although she genuinely loved the position of authority that moment offered. The children were a little afraid of her as she was a big, older woman, sort of alarming to look at. The turkey, dressing with walnuts, gravy, mashed potatoes, sweet potatoes, cranberry sauce, corn, peas, hot bread, all the desserts, the coffee brewing, the smell of the hot cinnamon apple cider—oh my, what a great Thanksgiving to remember, Mom's last. The twins were eleven years old then, November 22, 1979.

⁂

This year, Mitzi announced her engagement to Brian Hughes. He was a nice clean-cut young man and had many of the same interests as her dad. She was anxious to show Brian the old house and gardens. They had to wait until spring. Things would be thawed out by then. Mitzi, Brian, Marie, and Willie, Marie's boyfriend, drove down to Clayton and investigated the old place. It was the end of April when the girls returned, and they were jumping sideways.

"Mom, the flowers, the flowers, you won't believe the flowers!" Marie shouted.

Mitzi was shouting also, and it was kind of hard to understand both of them as they yelled simultaneously. The guys interpreted for them. Marie was always excitable, but I had always thought she would eventually grow out of it. The girls were dignified when the circumstances called for it. Some are just natural-born dignified folk. Back to the story!

Eventually, the roses were budding. The colors varied from bright red, yellow, white, and of course, Mom's favorite, dark pink. We always had flowers by our house in Tunis, but Grandmama's had a special feeling of ecstasy that nothing could duplicate. The fragrance was so strong in the air you breathed at Mother's when the roses were blooming, it was as intoxicating as anything you could imagine.

ॐ

As time passed, I became more curious. David and I decided to drive down to Clayton for the weekend. I called the Clayton Inn and reserved our little room.

My eyes filled with tears as I looked onto a garden of the most beautiful roses I had ever seen. I felt as though Mother had been back tending her little flowers as she once had. The breeze blew the fragrance through the air as before, and my whole being was full of joy for that moment. My husband felt it too. It's not wintertime, and summer will be coming soon. "I guess *it is a sign* that summer will be here soon when they look so perfect in the spring time," I said. David agreed with me. He loved Mom and Dad like his very own since he had lost his parents at an early age. They adored him too, especially because my only brother had been killed while working on heavy equipment. David was much like my brother, Donald Charles Lee, who had three names besides his last name. David had the same mild-mannered personality. I loved him with all my heart. David looked over his repair work on the trellises, archway, and lattices. Each one looked like a fine piece of artwork as the full bouquets and majestic red climbing roses stood out in all directions. Some bushes did look bedraggled, so David told me that he was going to drive up to Mr. Heater's Hardware for some string to support the droopy plants. I was not in the mood to be left alone at all.

David left so quickly that I didn't have time to protest. I was still in awe as I viewed all the wondrous flowers. I felt a little numb as my eyes focused on one dark pink rose bush.

I said aloud, "Mom, you are here because this rose bush is *too perfect*. You have to be here to nourish it. It wouldn't look this way if you weren't here." Hot tears began to flow. The very thing I didn't want to happen did happen. Suddenly, I felt a force or power, whatever you want to call it. I trembled. When I felt another warm breeze, I started to run, but then I stopped dead in my tracks. I asked myself, "Why should I be afraid of my own mother?"

~~

The odd feeling passed, and soon David was getting out of the van. He had a ball of string and proceeded to tie up the little plants. Each lovely flower was being carefully tended to. David was good at making any rosebush look its very best. The plants looked as if they said, "Thank you," as they leaned against each trellis for support. They were stretched out and spread evenly reaching upward toward the sky. There were several very bushy bushes. Many yellow roses were starting to bloom.

The Seven Sisters would take a little longer to bud. It was usually around the middle of May or first part of June before they bloomed. I did know all the mulching and good attending to would bring them back as good as new. We used our old coffee grounds as part of the mulch. Mother once told me that it was good for roses.

I was so inquisitive yet still a little uneasy. The curiosity made me do it! Well, the curiosity kept me there, observing each change, day by day. I wanted to see this little wonderland of blooming roses and blossoming garden. The fragrance was mind-boggling. There weren't many passersby. We were located too far off of the beaten path. I was getting more and more comfortable after each visit. I was relieved. You know how you want to get into a pool of water, but you have to test it before you do? Well, that's the only way I can describe what I was feeling. I needed to test the waters before I committed myself totally to this endeavor.

WHAT A *mess!*

The house had to be taken apart room by room. It was small but roomy with a great front porch. I hadn't gone into the house yet, but I entertained the thought of going into the house when I saw the wallpaper from the old bedroom lying on the ground. It was September, and time had flown by again. Much of the house had been refurbished already. Marie, Mitzi, and David had been the expert advice-givers. I would rather stay out of the planning and restoration process. I stepped aside. I didn't want direct involvement, but if I had the chance, I would peek over someone's shoulder now and then when the plans were lying exposed on the big construction table outdoors. I was slowly breaking down. All I could see was a *big mess!* What a mess! What a mess it was, was all I could see.

c⊙

My girls would come down and carry on about how wonderful it was looking around, and yet they were sensitive to my feeling as well. I believe they knew that I was healing through all of this. But as the old saying goes, it takes time, and some say time heals all wounds. I was still pondering on that one, and I did not want to be pushed into something before I was ready. I was still testing the water before diving into deep involvement.

c⊙

The garage that Dad built was still standing out back. It was in bad shape too. Parts of the old bee-hives were still behind the garage. Great Granddad had shown my dad how to get the bees, hives and all, out of the big trees in the woods and the hives would just *drop* into a big bag when Dad got the bee hives down. He had loved being able to share his memories of his grandfather with me. He said,

"Daughter, I was fifteen years old when Granddad showed me how to get that hive out of the tree in the little forest by the new cut hill. When that queen bee got on me, my granddad just laughed so hard watching me run like a scalded dog. I thought he was going to fall down laughing out loud. Instead, he laughed and helped me get away in the process. I had a lot of stings, though."

One thing my dad learned to do was handle those bees properly. We always had fresh honey. It was dark and so good. There was nothing like it.

David went into the old garage as he decided to help out the contractor and look for some sort of tool that he just knew my dad had at one time. Then I heard a loud voice shrieking for help from the garage. It was David. I froze. I hadn't gone into the garage either, but nothing or no one could hurt my family. If they tried, I turned into a fighting tigress or lioness! You can take your pick. All at once, I ran. I ran as fast as my legs would carry me. Without fear, I flung the door open, and I started cackling. I held my stomach, because it hurt to laugh that hard.

There was my poor husband, backed into a

corner. Tool in hand, and the most beautiful pole-cat—what you may refer to as a streamline kitty with a fluid drive, or *skunk*—hunched over on the other side of the building. The skunk wasn't paying a bit of attention to my dear sweetheart. She was taking care of her new babies. David shrank down and backed out of the side door ever so slowly without the tool he came to get.

As I glanced back into the garage, I saw a moving sight. There it was, the little red handprint where I had pressed my hand in Dad's paint can lid and then pressed it onto the great big post. The hand was so small. And there was my brother's on the other heavy post that held up this old barn of a garage. David had left me as he ran straight back to the cottage. I walked slowly back to the garden, recalling my brother's face and good times.

$\backsim$

When I returned to the flower garden, there wasn't much to do. The weeds were gone. The beautiful supports, borders, walks, and plant wells were all neatly trimmed and manicured. A picture or paint-ing could not have done it justice. Even though we lived modestly, Mother always said that flowers were free and would give you life if you let them. I thought about that as I sat on the cement patio bench Dad had made. It was cool to the touch.

"Life. That is what's happening to me—life. Mom, you were so right. I'm angry that I have to live here without you. I'm mad because I can't call you and be comforted! I want you back!" I cried.

Just then, someone was standing by my side. It was David. He had heard my cries. He embraced me as he let all the pain flow from me to him. It seemed like he took it all for me. It eased me to stand and be held by him. God sent him to comfort me. Only God knows how I ached in my heart, and he knew how to answer my prayers. When it seemed like I had exhausted all of my tears, I collected myself. I felt much better.

"Sometimes you just have to cry it out," my sweetheart said.

David took my hand and asked, "Are you ready to walk into the little house now?"

I took a deep breath. I had been trying to talk myself into this very moment for days. He told me we could wait if I wasn't ready, but I believed I could handle it. I had expected more work to be done, but all I could see was a mess. "What a mess, what a mess!" I exclaimed. Then we walked over the mess and entered the most beautiful little room in the whole world. It was Mom and Dad's front room. There was the great picture window Mom had always wanted but never had. It was letting in all the gorgeous sunshine. My girls had made sure that was included in the plans. The little fireplace and hearth looked brand new and cozy. I was so happy to see the job being done with such caution and care. I hadn't considered what my little family had done until that very moment. They were setting things straight for Mother. It would be the house that she always wanted and hadn't had. I still felt her presence and knew that she had to know about it somehow. Mom had always loved the little cottage, but the touches and changes she wanted when she and Dad were still here were never completed. When Dad left her, she didn't seem to care about fixing up the little house anymore. She wasn't too interested in any repairs or reaching the goals she set before Dad passed away. The desire was gone from her heart. Mother would say, "It's just not the same without your daddy to share life with, Trishy." She called me Trishy a lot. Then she would quote the Bible verbatim, "'But as it is written, Eye hath not seen, nor ear heard, neither have entered into the heart of man, the things which God hath prepared for them that love him,' 1 Corinthians 2:9."

After that she said, "Honey, this world is not my home, I'm only passing through, so don't weep for me when I'm gone. I have something greater waiting for me. Greater than this place or anything on earth." That's something I couldn't promise her, not to weep for her when she was gone.

As I remembered that, I still knew in my heart that she would have loved to have seen her dreams made a reality, and I wanted to make it happen for her. Mother would have wanted to know her grandchildren helped make her dream come to pass. Although, in my heart of hearts, I knew she was much happier than I was right then.

But how did David and the girls know how to do all of this? How to make all these wonderful changes as they rebuilt this place? I wondered if

I had talked about it too much or if they remembered Mom, her dreams, and loved her as I did.

"Yes, Mama, we remembered Grandmama," said Marie. Mitzi agreed with her sister and told me she just felt so good doing this project for our whole family, not just one of us. "After all, Mom, you always said, 'We come as a unit.'" I was so glad to know that my girls were mature and selfless. I couldn't have been more proud of them.

We walked carefully through each room. David held tightly to my hand and kept me from stepping on boards and nails. Mr. Dennis, our contractor, told me that the boards and nails would be cleaned up in a few days. They had to finish painting and then install the new flooring. My husband wanted me to see this one room nearly finished, the little front room with the fireplace I loved so, and they had had to stop everything else to accomplish that. It only needed a few last-minute touches, light fixtures, tiles, and carpet. I knew the girls had gone shopping for a large area rug like Mother used to have, but I hadn't seen it. It was so close to completion. I fell in love with this charming little place. The shock of relief left me feeling weak.

IT'S TIME TO MOVE ON,
girl, move on

I consoled myself after the trauma in the garage and the walk through of the wonderful little house by going to Mr. McNeilly's Ice Cream Parlor. It's more modern now, but still had that old-time atmosphere about it. Mr. Doug McNeilly was quiet and seemed to be in perfect peace at all times. I always felt settled after I had visited with him for a while. He didn't state his opinion too often, but when he did, you knew he would be his consistent logical self. He told me that I had been putting off this confrontation way too long, and I needed to grow up and enjoy my life while I was still able to do it. He reminded me of my dearest Aunt Rose and Mother. He called Mom by her name, Bethany. In fact, Mr. McNeilly was in a preachy mood. I had not seen him in a mood like that very much, maybe never! He gave me Scripture verse after verse to awaken my senses, reminding me that I was a child of God. He had been my Sunday school teacher when I was a young girl; perhaps much hadn't changed over the years. He knelt in his little ice cream parlor, took my hands in his, and prayed for me right then and there. It meant so much to me. I was so relieved.

He and his wife, Patty, were friends of both Mom and her younger sisters, Rose and Shirley. He said that no finer women walked the earth. He told me that God waited until the *roses were too perfect* and then He took them home where only real perfection could be placed in *his heavenly bouquet.*

Wow, I thought, *what a statement!* That gave me some real perspective. The lightbulb literally turned on and turned on bright! I hadn't considered something on that order. I could apply this to our rose garden too. The roses can't bloom to perfection until it is time for them to die so they can wake again. Then they can start the cycle all over once more with new life. I thought, *How keen of Mr. McNeilly.* He made me take a whole new account of my life in thirty minutes.

After his little speech, Mr. McNeilly walked casually back to his old-fashioned soda fountain and asked me if I wanted a refill of my delicious root beer float.

I said, "Maybe not, you have given me something far richer to take in. Thanks. I'll be seeing you."

Waving goodbye, he said, "I'll see you later, Trish."

$\backsim$

My heart pounded as I skipped to the Clayton Inn. David was wanting his supper. The girls had driven down to the Krazy Korner Café in Millerville to get a bite to eat. It was about ten miles away. I surprised him with my happiness. He was thrilled and started to tease me like he had used to. I just giggled and couldn't quit chuckling. I felt so good. David told me if a visit with a little old man could make me change this much, I should have a dose of Mr. McNeilly at least once a week. I agreed. He was amazed. The depression that he had expected and had lived with continuously wasn't there. It was gone! Vanished! I felt as if I had been delivered from some oppressing, heavy, bad spirit of some sort. I thanked God for this joy that entered in where sadness had dwelt and occupied so much of my heart.

Since the girls had the van, we had to wait until they came back to go anywhere to eat as I hadn't prepared anything ahead of time. Besides that, I wanted to celebrate. I called a friend of mine, Phyllis Hancock, and we decided to go to Marion for a nice dinner at the Steak House Restaurant where we could relax, sit, and just enjoy being served. Phyllis was happy to go with us. She wasn't married, but we knew Mr. Right would be coming into her life soon. David and I enjoyed her company. Phyllis worked at the Village Hall, known as the Town Hall, but since Clayton wasn't that large, it was referred to as a village. She collected the water bills, etc. We were old school chums.

Dinner was very good. My baked potato could have been cooked a little longer. Other than that, it was great. Phyllis especially enjoyed the time we spent together. She kept bringing up my folks and memories of long ago. David learned a few things that I wasn't sure I wanted him to know, but he seemed elated to be informed of my dumb antics. He liked hearing about me getting caught in the fifth grade, when I sat behind Brenda in class, for a prank I pulled. Brenda's hair always hung down on my desk. She liked to fling her braids back until they hit me right in the face. She wanted me to notice her long, silky black mane. I told her she had horse hair. I wasn't very nice at all. I got caught because I just didn't think ahead. I forgot that the glue was on my desk and not Johnny's. I was intending on letting him take the blame because he loved getting other people in trouble. I stuck her braids into the glue bottle and pressed them down on the tip end of my desk. Time passed as we read our assignments. The recess bell ran. When Brenda tried to stand up, she got about three quarters of the way and then fell back into her seat. She thought someone was pulling her hair. She turned to give somebody a piece of her mind when she tumbled down. Her desk fell sideways with her. My desk tilted forward, but I sat down hard, and her hair pulled free. Brenda screamed like a wild cat. I was gazing at a lot of the frazzled mess still stuck to my desk as Mr. Jones looked down at me tapping his foot rapidly. I had to write, "I will not glue Brenda's hair to my desk again," one hundred times on the chalkboard. My wrist felt like it would fall apart before I was through writing; and oh yes, there was no recess for me. I never did that little trick again.

Phyllis remembered this story in detail. She and David laughed themselves silly. That wasn't the only little incident that she remembered, but I won't go into that now. I didn't know that the whole class was so happy about Brenda's mishap. She was hard to get along with, so most of the classmates were glad to see her have an embarrassing moment for once. Phyllis continued with her funny memories. We talked and laughed. That was something I hadn't done for a long time. I was taught that laughter did your heart good like a medicine. I believe that's true. I felt so much better.

Our evening was over much too soon, but I promised that it would happen more often. We rested well that night.

$\backsim$

I was up bright and early the next day. I made coffee, and low-sodium bacon smelled all throughout the little kitchenette. Everyone woke to a hungry feeling in their tummies. I cooked breakfast with a happy sensation deep within. I felt a definite change, a change for the better. Everyone could feel it, and everyone was glad—especially me. It was time to move on and leave the grief behind. I tried to look for the things that would bring me smiles. Life is better when you do that. It's too short to feel sorry for yourself for so long. I still had a family too, and Mother and Dad wouldn't want me to be unhappy, although they weren't there to tell me so; I knew life's lessons they had instilled in me. I had a family to live for. Mama would have said in her *snappy* little way, "It's time to move on, girl, move on!"

GETTING BACK
to reality

After the positive experience I had in Clayton, life seemed to take a turn for the worse in Tunis. My best friend, Sue, became very ill. We hadn't been as close as we had in the past due to me being gone, and probably a few other things. It didn't seem like 1991. Time goes by so quickly and another year is gone before you know what has happened. Sue's job was in jeopardy because of the days she had missed due to being ill. She asked me if I would fill in for her. Her four-year-old son, Joey, was having a hard time dealing with his mother's illness. He needed to feel the closeness of her presence more than ever. The doctors told Sue that she would have to stop working for a while and let her body rest in order to take the treatment she would need later on. Sue was a hard worker, and I didn't know if I could fill her shoes. Her boss and I talked things over. He was convinced that I could do the job. I wouldn't be as proficient as Sue, but if it meant helping her, I would do that.

As time went on, Sue worsened. She needed a bone marrow transplant. The hospital could not find a match. It had been six months, and they hadn't found a suitable donor. David, Mitzi, Marie, and I volunteered to be tested. All of the tests turned out negative.

This was so hard for us to deal with. We wanted to help her, but we couldn't. Sue was like a part of our family. She was always there for us. We couldn't stand seeing her so sick and our hands literally tied. She was married to a great guy. David and Larry Jacob were friends. We called him Jake. His test was negative too. When everyone else was sick of hearing David discuss his computer business, Jake would always listen. Even if he didn't understand a word David was saying, Jake was there. He was a true friend.

I thought, *Dear God, what are we going to do?*

We can't live without Sue. Depression was working on me once again. I had to talk to someone. But whom could I go to? I finally thought of the first people I should have gone to, our pastor and his wife.

Sue was going downhill fast. My aunt hadn't survived that disease. She only lived a few months after her diagnosis. So my friend had done well for the situation, hanging on with every fiber of her being. Faith in knowing that God knew what he was doing kept her alive. My pastor and his wife were supportive and talked with me about the release of Mom's pain and made sense of a lot of things. I appreciated their concern.

They told me to think positively about this situation with our dear friend Sue and to believe in the Scriptures I was taught, knowing that I should lean on the Lord and not my own understanding. We found this in Proverbs 3:5. I know I am supposed to trust God and not put my confidence in man or other people entirely, so I made up my mind to follow their advice. And I knew it would be better as I *trusted and leaned* on Jesus, and we prayed together. I questioned myself and wondered, *What do people do without the Lord?* I felt so much better after I left those two great people.

_ℰ͜ᗞ_

David and Jake were at our house when I returned. I had cooked a pot of beans before leaving for the pastor's house. They were helping themselves to the beans and fried potatoes. I still needed to make the cornbread, but they were too hungry to wait on that. My husband always said I made a mean pot of beans. Jake hadn't had an appetite since Sue was put into the hospital. Joey was even eating. Jed, a friend of David's, had even dropped in and had a bowl of beans. This seemed odd to me. I hoped I hadn't been reading the signals wrong. It was a feeling of happiness in this room. I'm sure!

David stopped eating for a brief moment to let me know that Sue had a donor. Yes, it was true! I immediately remembered the pastor's words and thanked God for the prayer being answered before I made it home. When I arrived at the Tunis General Hospital the next day, Sue had already received the necessary treatment for the transplant procedure. She was in the recovery room. Dr. Robinson let me go look at her. She didn't budge. She was out like a light.

As I gazed upon this angel and frail form lying before me, I thought, *Oh no, the rose is too perfect,* and then was reminded of the pastor's words once again. "You must know when you believe, you must know that you know that you know." In other words, *believe what you pray when you pray and know that God exists. You know it in your heart and soul.* I fought the nervous feeling once again.

Sue awoke feeling somewhat disoriented. I tried to reassure her. She stared directly into my eyes and giggled a little as she said, "Trish, as long as I've known you, I was the one to try to keep you up and out of the gloomy, mully grubs. Now it's your turn! By the way, don't make too many mistakes on my job for me to clean up, okay?" She dozed off again with a big grin on her face.

That made my day. Jake and Joey laughed too. They were standing right behind me. Each one of us had a stream of tears running down our faces. Mine dripped down on Sue's face. She was right, you know. They were tears of joy.

Sue recuperated, and later as she underwent

the real transplant, the bone marrow did its job. She was in complete remission when she went back for her last test results. We were so grateful to the Lord.

Time passed, and Sue was back on her feet as good as new. I was happy to give her job back. It was fun for a change, but the reason I was doing it wasn't so pleasing. She was a medical receptionist. It took a terrible incident like this to draw us as close as we should have already been.

ॐ

Our house was a disaster after working down south for one year. We had to fix up our place in Tunis. Mitzi was working right along, although she was keeping a lot of her personal feelings inside. Mitzi was one to dig out information from someone. I think she should have been a lawyer and not merely a legal assistant, which is an important position. But she had it in her to be a good attorney, and I knew that. Mitzi would be out of school soon. A job was waiting for her if she wanted it. She had told her sister that she thought of moving to Grandmama and Grandpapa's place if I would say it was all right. Of course, she was afraid to mention it to me before I had really gone over everything and reasoned out all the pros and cons. Mitzi didn't know how I would feel, especially with her career. She had spoken with Mr. Cox, and he was already making plans for her to join him in his practice.

Marie had shut the door after Sue and Jake left. I was picking up the dinner plates when she spurted out, "Mom, hasn't Mitzi told you anything?" I glanced at her with a puzzled look as she continued, "Do you know what she's up to?"

"No," I said. "I don't, so why don't you tell me, as long as you aren't disclosing a confidence or if it's to let me know she's in harm's way somehow."

"All right, I will since you asked. You see, it's like this: Mitzi has been dreaming of living in Grandmama's cottage since the first day we started work in the garden. She wants to live there and work for Mr. Cox. She's even told him about it. He thinks it is a great idea. Now, what do you think of that?" Marie was curious about my reaction when she revealed this bit of information. However, she was as cool and calm as a cucumber.

This was a lot to take in one lump sum. David walked in midstream of the conversation, and we both stood there with our mouths wide open. I was flabbergasted but happy. It was a dream of mine, of course, that one of my children would actually experience some of the wonderful moments and memories I once had. There wouldn't be any more strangers living there. Our daughter would be in a nice, safe place, where she felt secure and happy. Oh, what a wonderful thought. Her father and I loved the idea. But why hadn't Mitzi spoken to us? Did Brian know? How did he feel about it? I would try to bring up the subject in a nonchalant way.

My heart ached. I wondered why my daughter couldn't come to me. She had even gone to someone else to discuss her secret. Her dad and I had a heart-to-heart talk with our sweet Melissa Renée. She answered all of our questions. She was the quiet one unless she was doing some research for an attorney. She could speak up when the time called for it. Mitzi was very understanding and knew that God's Word tells us "To every thing there is a season, and a time to every purpose under the Heaven" (Ecclesiastes 3:1). She quoted that to us and told us that she was waiting for the right time to tell us. One reason she didn't tell us was, Mitzi considered my nerves and the sadness she felt when I was at Grandmama's. The next reason was, Brian did know and was not opposed to the idea, but first he needed to get a job. They had waited until the job was secure and Mr. Heater had already spoken to him about managing the store. Mr. Heater was getting tired and needed the extra help. He was having trouble with his eyes.

But before they could get married, which was their next plan of action, all these things had to be in place. David and I were elated to know all of this. Truly, there is a time for all things under the sun. All things work together when you are striving to do the right thing and everyone's mind is in one accord.

Brian wanted to spend their honeymoon in Branson, Missouri, where some of his family lived, and then spend the rest of their lives at the Scarbrough Cottage and Gardens. Mitzi added that she would have to get her *dad or someone* to come help with the gardens because with her fingernails and all, well, you get it. Besides, she had a job too. I thought of what a gift it would be to give my parents.

David thought, *Dad or someone, my eye!* He wasn't about to let anyone else disturb his little paradise now!

Just knowing my parents' grandchildren and maybe their great grandchildren would be living in their little home was dreamlike.

This little talk had been a real enlightenment. David and I told her it was up to her and it sounded like her plans were set in place already. Her happiness was all I wanted, and I couldn't be happier.

REMEMBERING DAYS IN
the country

Oh, how precious are the memories. I began to tell my girls about the wonderful times I had as a child. How their grandpapa had a small orchard on the other side of the cottage. I would climb into the trees and eat my fill of peaches, apples, pears, plums, or cherries, whichever fruit was ready. We also had grapes that hung full and juicy not far from the rose garden. I didn't care for some of my mama's cooking because she and Daddy were raised eating a lot of pork. Mom liked to cook it all the time. I especially did not like pork steak. Somehow, Mama could find an excuse at least once a week to fix pork steak. When I smelled it cooking, I would head for one of the fruit trees.

Needless to say, it was probably one of the best things I ever did for myself.

Mother had chickens that laid eggs, and we never bought store eggs. Dad's bees always gave us honey. My, we lived on meager fare. But I never felt poor. My life was rich with love, and every need was met.

I had been a sickly child, and God had had mercy on my life. Only through the prayers of Mother, Father, and those who really had a relationship with the Lord did I survive. I spent the first year of my life under an oxygen tent in the hospital in St. Louis, Missouri. I weighed twelve pounds, and that was the one thing that happened in a positive way. I had gained from four pounds to twelve pounds in one year on glucose. One day a miracle happened, and the doctors had to give the credit to *a higher power,* because nothing they had done had any effect on me or made any change. The day of the *miracle* made a great change in the life of my parents. They served God in their church from then on and were giving and loving to all those who seemed to need it. I grew up in this special place and home, so as anyone can see, I was very privileged to be one chosen to live and serve the Lord.

The girls had heard that story many times before. However, they seemed to always be interested each time it was told. I told them about the days when it was warm and my dog, Penny, and I would walk down the railroad tracks across the way. I would find pennies and all kinds of change lying in between the wood trestles. Then I would bring it home and hide it in my little glass jar in the closet.

Across the railroad was the place where my other grandparents had a large home. It had long since burned to the ground, and nothing was left. A homeless man lived by there. Everyone called him Zeke. He had a horse and wagon. Zeke came around to everyone's place from time to time to collect pieces of iron or bits of metal you might want hauled off, and people would pay him to take it off. He was a mysterious fellow to me. I wondered how he lived. When I was about eleven years old, my friend Mary Ruth and I decided to peek at his living quarters. Mother had always warned me to stay away from old Zeke's place, but we just had to know! My grandfather had owned a lot of land and this piece across the tracks was part of it. He was a business man, and it was named Webster's Grove for my grandfather, Matt Webster. When grandfather was still living, people came on Sunday afternoons for picnics, and in the winter they skated on the frozen pond. This place had a lot of beautiful trees besides the huge pond where ducks gathered all year round. It was so sad to look at and know he had lost it all. He had lost it before I was born. I only grew up hearing the beautiful stories about it. No one lived there now except the animals and Zeke. In a manner of speaking he just homesteaded for a while by the pond.

It was sunny on the day Mary Ruth and I had gotten so inquisitive about his place. We just wondered how he lived, ate, and slept. His horse and wagon were gone, so we thought it would be a perfect time for a little peep. We thought of it more as an investigation than prying. Really now! Anyway, we were so uneasy when we approached the little lean-to of a shack, we were nearly shaking. Mary Ruth just looked in and ran. I looked about five seconds more, and that was it. We saw a little building made of odd-sized boards with huge cracks. Also a mat on the ground; no floor; a couple shelves on the wall, if you could call it a wall, with a few cans of food on one shelf. I don't even recall the food labels. Boy, did we run and get in high gear in a hurry to get away from there. I believe it was shear guilt. We were doing something we weren't supposed to do.

We never told our folks. But each time Zeke passed by with his horse and wagon, I just knew he knew what we did. Mary Ruth and I were blood sisters and would never tell.

e

Another story I recalled was when the lady who lived just a few houses away would ask me to baby-sit her little ones. She had two sweet little baby girls. The funny thing was she was the one whom my mother had trusted to babysit me when I was little. It wouldn't be for long, but she was a dear young girl Mother had known all her life. Her name was Mary Ann. There was a song that was popular when I was a little girl called "Mary Ann, Down by the Seashore Sifting Sand." I am not sure that's the correct title, but I remember hearing it and thinking they were singing about my Mary Ann.

She eventually got married and had her children. I spent time with her and her family whenever I could. It was fun. Since I had no siblings at home, she took the place of one. My brother was older and left home when I was very young. I loved fixing her dark black hair up into a French twist. She let me play like that. Sometimes her husband and she would invite neighbors over for a sing-a-long with guitars and wienie roast.

Trudy, her niece, was often over there too. Once, she and I found this long dried-out weed. It had little fuzzy things inside of it and was about as big as our little finger. I don't recall what they were called. I used to know. Mary Ann said, "You know you can smoke those, don't you?" I was fifteen by then and knew better than to do something that sinful. However, we believed her and just wanted to see what happened if we tried it. Sure enough, while the bonfire was blazing, we broke off a piece of that weed, dipped the end of it into the fire, turned to where no one could see us, and watched it light up. It burned slowly. We both took our turns taking short puffs and blowing the smoke out, thinking about how grown up we must look. We really thought we got away with it, but I was getting sick to my stomach, and Trudy never told me what happened to her. As it turned out, somehow my mom and dad got wind of what I had done, and I really wished I wouldn't have considered it.

Boy, was I preached to about all the ill effects that could have on me and how it could have been poison, etc. I didn't try it again. I know Mary Ann didn't intend for us to do that; she was just telling us about it. Being sick and with all the apologies to my folks, Mary Ann, and God, I never had a desire to do that again. I was soon well.

The country air was clean, void of smoke, unless someone was burning a pile of leaves in the fall. That aroma was welcome but didn't last long. When I was young, the country was free of smog. There is nothing like living with such wonderful memories of a wholesome time. I rode my bike, went horseback riding, and fished sometimes without fear of being abducted by some creep. Now, we were cautious and not completely unaware or oblivious to harmful acts of some individuals, but life was peaceful in the country when I was growing up. When I wasn't helping my mother or dad, a lot of my time was dedicated to daydreaming. Life in the country was easy and slow paced compared to nowadays, and I loved it.

So many stories to tell but never enough time. The girls were ready to go home when I finished telling them about my cousin Peggy's horse that would never pass the apple orchard without stopping and getting his tummy full.

RESTORATION *completed*

One whole exhausting, wonderful year had passed. It was October again. This was the day of reconciliation. I would face the nightmare that had plagued me so. I would walk into Scarbrough Cottage and see the beautiful work that had been done on the home, lawn, and also the landscaping with the trees and all the shrubs. The orchard would take more time. However, that project would eventually be achieved. The garden had been overwhelming, but I knew I had to see the rest of the accomplishments. The way I consoled myself, besides prayer and knowing God had changed me, was knowing it was really my daughter's house now, and that was the key that unlocked everything. Mother would be so thrilled to know what had been done. She told me that breaking strong ties was hard to do. The ties I had to her would never be broken. The changes would give me space to accept what I couldn't change. It was getting easier and easier; each step I took was a step forward and not backward.

As I walked onto the lawn, I saw the trim around the sidewalk that led up to the front porch steps. It was straight for a short distance and then curved just as my dad had originally made it to curve. He said I could roller skate and have fun on this walk. It slanted just enough for me to roll without much effort. I did spend many happy hours doing just that when I was young. I continued walking, absorbing each change and things that had been added, replaced, and redone from the roof to the ground.

I stepped onto the deck and looked at porch swing, which survived since it was metal. It had been painted. Willie and Brian sanded it as smooth as silk. They spray painted it to match the trim on the house and the shutters. It looked fresh and new, but I remembered the days when Mother and I sat there shelling those peas. Pictures of the past kept sweeping through the windows of my mind—1700 square feet looked much smaller than I remembered. The girls had gotten the guys involved in this project before they knew what hit them. Everyone was enthusiastic. I was surprised that I hadn't felt the sadness. I thought I might feel a little more upset, but instead there was joy in its place.

Now, to open the front door. The solid oak door had been restored. David and the girls stood behind me. They watched as I slowly turned the knob and walked inside. I wasn't sad at all but so full of joy that it just overflowed. I felt it through and through. My eyes fell on the fireplace Dad first built and the rocker in the corner of the room. The walls were all textured white. The ceiling lights and wall lamps were glistening. They were so clean. All of Mom's hanging strings to pull on her ceiling lights were gone. New electrical wall outlets replaced the old hanging strings. I continued to the dining room where the new light fixture hung. It was just right for the room, formal and elegant, just what Mother loved. On I went to the kitchen. All the new wall cabinets formed above the countertop and around the room like a large L shape. Everyone followed quietly behind me as I examined each room. The bedrooms were almost like they were when I was growing up. A hard pain hit my heart, but then it left as a light feeling entered. They used wallpaper on one wall in the master bedroom. The beautiful roses appeared sparingly on it. One wall had lovely new sliding-mirror closet doors. This made everything look bigger, and it really was larger than it was when Mother and Dad were living here.

Mother always wanted a dusty rose carpet in her bedroom where her beautiful vanity still sat. The guys had even restored this gorgeous piece of furniture. I had spent hours just piddling with bobby pins, jewelry, and the like, sitting at Mama's vanity. The mirror had a few little worn places that were barely visible. The beauty of the vanity itself shadowed any defects in the large mirror. It was made of walnut, and the grain flowed from each drawer, across the top and the sides. It was too nice to get rid of, as was the chest of drawers that matched it. What a sight for sore eyes! I just couldn't believe it. The tears trickled down my cheeks, but I was just fine.

Suddenly, the silence was broken when Brian and Willie drove up and stomped upon the porch. They rang the doorbell and proceeded to venture on in. David had installed a new refrigerator, dishwasher, washer, and dryer. The house only had one bathroom, but we had extended beyond our budget for the time being, so the extra bath would have to come later. Willie and Brian had brought some groceries, paper plates, and cups. I was still in a daze about all of this but glad the guys thought ahead about food because that was the last thing on my mind, that's for sure.

The little kitchen had a lunch bar extending from the countertop. Mother had a very long table for the dining area, and it was taken to the dumps during the gutting of the place. This place wasn't ready for occupants just yet. There wasn't much furniture to speak of, except for the rocker, and Mother and Dad's bedroom set. No beds yet, chairs, tables, etc., but for now, we could celebrate the renovation of this old cottage. The electricity was on, and my hubby had made coffee. I felt good about this beautiful place. It was all Mother would have wanted and more. It was warm and cozy. The big window was overlaid with ruffled lace curtains, and it would let in all the cheery sunshine. You could see for miles down the road if the rose bushes on the front yard fence didn't grow too high. And now, just to think of my grandchildren being raised here, if we had any that is, it was just so wonderful. The *real restoration* had been completed—*in me, Trisha Elaine Scarbrough Gleaton.*

LET'S GET *together*

I was thinking about Thanksgiving again. This time we were feeling a lot better. If we had the furniture in the cottage, we could go to Clayton for Thanksgiving this year, November 1992. The closer the holiday came, the more I realized that the little cottage wouldn't be ready for us. Maybe we could make it next year.

Sue, Jake, Joey, and Phyllis came for Thanksgiving at our house in Tunis. It was full with the rest of the family. The pastor and his wife, Martha, came for the meal, and we enjoyed each other's company.

After dinner, Pastor, David, and the guys went outdoors for their gab time as they played basketball on the small court by the garage. They looked funny dressed in hoodies and sneakers bouncing that ball. It was getting pretty cold now, but they were tough. They liked to be classed as macho, *real men!*

The ladies talked over old times and discussed when we would get together again and go shopping. The coffee was so good with one more piece of pecan pie. I added a little ice cream too. Mitzi said that Dolly and Mary would want to go with us to the big sale at the mall. I wasn't interested in shopping until after Christmas. Bigger sales! Maybe I wouldn't go until February. I usually started shopping in August, and by the time Christmas arrived, I had completed my shopping long before.

My friends had noticed the big change in me. They all spoke about my big personality turnabout. I was glad but had hoped I wasn't such a stick-in-the-mud.

Everyone was kind enough to say, "Well, you weren't the happiest person I've known, but we loved ya anyway."

One friend said jokingly, "Trish, we knew you were going through hard times. And you can't really judge a person until you've walked in their shoes, so I always thought of that when I had any thoughts of shaking you a time or two."

I know a person speaks from the abundance of their heart. I believe I just felt sorry for myself. I'm so glad I came out of that state of mind.

Some of our neighbors—Ken, Bobby, and Sarah—dropped by. They didn't come over often because they were aware of David's business and my writing. We were more or less hermits when we were concentrating on our work. Connie and Reba walked down with part of their leftover desserts. They were sisters. I put on some more coffee and tasted the cream cheese cake and pumpkin bread cheese roll. They had a thing about cheeses this year. It was good, but one small bite was all I could afford. Since I had gotten happier, so had my waistline. That meant I had an appetite and ate more, therefore the waistline was a few inches thicker now! My face seemed like I had a permanent smile pasted on it. I loved feeling so good and happy. I kept telling myself, *The joy of the Lord is my strength,* even if I didn't say it out loud.

Kathryn and Edward came over since it looked

like were having a family reunion. They were old friends. Sherry came with them, and she wasn't empty-handed either. The fresh homemade yeast bread smelled divine, and it tasted that way too. We used to always get together with our neighbors for part of the day on Thanksgiving. It was nice to feel like visiting again.

I couldn't remember when we last had so much talking and noise in our house. With everything we had undergone this past year, we had plenty of conversation to share with everyone. I repeated the story so many times that I felt like I should have just put an article in the *Daily Star* or had a special broadcast tell it all at one time.

When the guys came in and the last guests were gone, I thought I would let the pans soak because they wouldn't all fit in the dishwasher anyway.

It was nice to go up the stairs to my big fluffy bed and curl up for the night. It's so nice when we *get together,* but *oh,* so good when they all went home.

MELISSA (MITZI), HER WEDDING, THE GARDEN, *and brian*

Everyone mentioned the good air and how nice the home and all the remodeling looked. The roses were perfect but not too perfect. The heat was starting to make the petals turn a little, but we trimmed all the brown edges off so they looked fresh. The fragrance was intoxicating. As each guest arrived for Mitzi and Brian's wedding, they were given a little tour of Scarbrough Cottage and the grounds. The white covered chairs were placed just outside the lovely space. The path through the center of the garden led directly to the podium where the minister stood waiting for the bride and groom. Sue played the keyboard softly as we watched and were so captivated by the event we were about to witness.

Mitzi and Brian were getting married early in the day at Scarbrough Cottage in the rose garden on Saturday, June 5, 1993. The great willow tree was so large that it shaded the very spot where the couple and minister were standing. The archway, filled with white wisteria draping from top to bottom with other flowers mingled in between, was breath-taking in itself. A nice breeze blew just as the ceremony began.

Our little Melissa Renée Gleaton was given in marriage that day by her father and me. I have no words to describe her beauty combined with the surroundings. The professional photographers we hired could not do this setting justice. They came close, but not perfect. No words could depict the picture I saw in my mind. Mitzi and the garden— she fit in flawlessly. The roses *were* too perfect— once we had them trimmed. She was the rose that day and she *was perfect.* She wore a white satin gown with a long train. She chose to carry the most beautiful bouquet of roses from the garden that you have ever seen. Her sister was dressed in a dark pink taffeta and chiffon dress with a burgundy sash, as were the other bridesmaids. Marie was the maid of honor, and she had a little extra touch to her dress. Her ribbon in front hung much longer from her waist than the others. Mitzi wanted everything decorated burgundy, pink, and white.

Mr. Lamb's wife was the Clayton florist. She arranged the bridal bouquet straight from the garden. So they were so fresh, big, and pretty. These roses seemed to know they had to be so lovely *for such a time as this.* The flower girl's rose petals were fresh from the garden as well. Everything was so nice. Mitzi's gown had scallops gathered twelve inches apart all the way around the bottom of the full satin skirt. The train was attached at the waist with a bow covering the greater part of her little backside. She was so tiny that the dress made her look even smaller. She had long sleeves to a point on the top of her hands. Her veil of illusion hung to her waist. It had a tiara that crowned her head with beads and small baby's breath from the garden. Her hair looked lighter as the sun shone directly on the long shimmering blanket of golden waves. Pastor was careful as he touched her head and Brian's when he said the prayer. I'm sure there was not a dry eye on the grounds.

Sue and Jake interrupted my thoughts with the words "What a little doll!" That's what I was thinking too. I was praying also for her happiness and health as I watched her handsome father proudly walk her to this enraptured young man. We knew he would be good to her. We would have a son now. He already called us Mom and Dad. It always felt right. We were proud of how he worked and made sure they had stability before they were married. It told us a lot about him. He sure looked handsome too. Brian was standing straight and tall with his white tux, dark pink, or I should say burgundy, tie, and cummerbund. He really objected when he was told the wedding colors were pink and white because he's a down-to-earth kind of guy. Pink? Anyway, when he saw it was so dark that it really was more of a burgundy color, he was all right with the choice.

Marie looked almost as if she were the bride. Her dress was full and came just below the knee. Mitzi also asked two of her closest friends to be bridesmaids. They were dressed just like Marie, only their sashes weren't as long as hers. Their hosiery was matched with sparkles. The shoes and elbow-length satin gloves matched the gorgeous dresses. The best man and groomsmen matched Brian. They wore white tuxedos with long tails.

Then I heard the words as the minister spoke, "Do you, Brian James Hughes, take Melissa Renée Gleaton to be your lawful wedded wife?" I broke out into a cold sweat and started to feel a little faint, but I was a trooper that day. I made it through without a lot of crying, and if I did shed a tear, it was for joy, not sorrow. Her big, brave daddy shed a few tears too. It was because of how proud he was of his little girl, I'm sure.

It seemed as though I was watching a fairy tale. My daughter being married in my mother's rose garden and the unbelievable truth of this happening was too much to embrace inside my soul. It was Mitzi's now. Grandmama and she shared the same love for those roses, as I did.

Phyllis caught the bridal bouquet.

The wedding reception took place at Town Meeting Hall. It wasn't that huge because the town isn't very big itself, but it seemed like a wonderful crowded auditorium of family and friends. Everyone always celebrated the important occasions there, like family reunions and this sort of occurrence. Cathie and Natasha, Melissa's dear friends, helped decorate. They did a wonderful job.

I wished the world could have seen her cake. Her friend Traci made it. She embellished it with fresh red rose petals from the garden. The petals were spread around the cake sparingly but perfectly. It was fascinating. The little seventeen-hundred-square-foot cottage was just a bit too small for all the wedding guests to gather inside or we would have had the reception there.

∞

When it was all over, we settled down. David and I returned to our routine in Tunis. Mitzi and Brian took a short trip to Branson, Missouri, for their honeymoon. They would take time for a longer, lovelier honeymoon when they saved their money and planned it out. Mitzi went to work for Mr. Cox. She was doing very well. Brian's ideas for Mr. Heater were difficult for Mr. Heater to grasp, but he did listen and try to tolerate Brian's enthusiasm.

Orville Cox, Mitzi's boss, had told Mr. Heater that Brian would take a lot of pressure off him. Brian knew business. He was excellent with bookkeeping. Of course, his brand new father-in-law would give him access to any computer or program that he might need. He would start keeping books right away. The way things were changing with the Internet, there were so many more options nowadays to help get all the accounts, present and past, updated and in order. Mr. Heater wasn't too *hip* on these new ideas.

This self-taught, older, well-informed store owner always gave credit to those who needed to pay up in a day or two. And sometimes it would lead to a bit longer, but he generally received what was due him within a reasonable time. He was accustomed to conducting his business with the folks in a friendly, warm sort of way. Mr. Heater always knew how to work out some sort of deal with anyone who was in earnest and trying to pay their bill, even if they offered him a portion of their crops.

This new computer stuff was contrary to his way of thinking, but if Orville Cox thought he should try out the new deal for a while, well, he supposed that he could adjust. However, if it didn't work out, he would go back to his old way of doing things and that right fast!

GREAT TIMES
to come

Church was a vital part of my life. I was always involved in every function I could be in, going to revivals, leading songs when I could, teaching Sunday school, taking the youth on church trips to the lake. But after losing my mother and as the years passed, I grew darker inside. I couldn't see the light of the Lord shining through. I was blinded to the good things. I couldn't get connected with my church. Pastor and his wife were always offering opportunities as they noticed me slipping backwards. I would make excuses as the weeks slipped by, one by one. I was tired and had to catch up on my business at home, or something was always hurting. You know, excuses, excuses. An old saying tells us: you can't see the forest for the trees. When you are in the very middle of a situation, it's hard to decipher your whereabouts, and that applied to my life. Even though I knew this, I ignored all the signs.

I kept myself busy with my business now, and with the girls gone, David working more, I was too wrapped up in myself. The depression had definitely gone and I felt happy most of the time now, but there was that little emptiness. I attributed it to my little family being spread in different directions and not under my own roof. The enemy is sly and doesn't want us to realize that our real need is in our *spiritual* life. I was blinded to that or tried to just overlook that fact.

I just quit reading God's Word, so when the enemy came at me like a flood, I had no answer. Jesus used the Word of God against the devil when he took Jesus up to the top of the temple and told Jesus to throw himself down. It's like my Sunday school teacher told me, the devil knows the Bible better than you and me. He knew who Jesus was before you or me. But Jesus knew how to fight him. He used the Word. Each time his answer was "It is written."

I finally went to a meeting at the church to apologize to our pastor and other church members because they all depended on me so much. They were all so understanding, but I could feel this undercurrent. It's like something is going on, but you can't quite put your finger on it. Little did I know how much they loved me and were praying for my family and me. They had fasted and prayed for our situation. I can't explain what that did for me when I was told about that.

One person said in the meeting, "Sister Trisha, you are going to see greater times, and they will come." That was pure faith. I tried believing, and I knew that person meant every word. I felt chills run up and down my arms and on the back of my neck. I really knew it would happen, but like Moses in the Old Testament, I needed someone to hold up my arms for me. I guess this was the time I needed that. You know, it happened, as I got back into God's Word and my prayer time. I was so blessed. I was able to focus on my duties at church again. I did even more for God's Work. I always wanted to be a help and not a hindrance. I did see that I had greater times to come. The latter was greater than the former. "The glory of this latter house shall be greater than of the former, saith the Lord of hosts: and in this place will I give peace, saith the Lord of hosts" (Haggai 2:9).

MY SILLY EMOTIONS AND
a bundle of joy

I visited my children at least once a month. Marie Annette Gleaton graduated with honors on Friday, May 27, 1994. We were so proud as we watched this lovely young girl blossom into an educated young woman anyone would be glad to call their daughter. She now had her degree and would be on staff at Tunis General Hospital as one of their most brilliant new interns. Also, we had a close eye on her little romance. It seemed to be more intense since her sister's marriage. We weren't too worried. She changed her mind a lot and was too excitable to be a married woman just yet. Not only that, her career was far too important to her at this point.

As time slipped by, Mitzi and Brian had continued to give the little cottage its final touches. It looked great. It was comfortable. I finally relaxed as I sat in the rocker by the small hearth.

When David, Jake, Joey, Sue, my neighbor Gale, and I decided to bring down the works for a barbeque and homemade ice cream one Saturday afternoon, I found myself walking with Joey to show him the McCrite's duck pond. No one was at home. Their son, Jerry, was the owner of this little farm since Joe and Miss Lizzie were gone now. I supposed Jerry had gone in for grain for his animals. The duck pond had always been one of my favorite spots. The McCrites had a sweet little arched bridge built over the pond. You could walk to the center and see the ducks swim underneath. It was cool. Joey and I carefully walked upon the bridge. It was still in good shape. I suppose Jerry enjoyed keeping the place up. It looked nice. The bridge looked as if it had a fresh coat of brown paint. You could smell it too.

I told Joey about Miss Lizzie giving me sacks of popcorn to feed the ducks when I was a little girl. I had even named those silly little waddling waders: Piggy, Po Thing, and Big Mama. Piggy always saw me coming with the sack of freshly-popped corn from a mile away. He was the first one every time. Big Mama graciously waddled up the little bank to me and ate from my hand. She was older and more settled. You could pet her too. Po Thing seemed to be so slow that most everything was gone before he would get some. Three or four more would gather around, but I didn't name them. I only named the ones that left a big impression on me, the ones with personality. I called all the others "Baby."

Joey and I talked as we walked off the bridge. He asked me where those ducks were right now. I told him that they must be off visiting family because they weren't there. Joey was satisfied with my answer. Just then some ducks with green heads started up the bank to greet us. "Wow, Aunt Trish, it's just like you told me. Here they come!" He was seven years old now and still called me Aunt Trish, even though we weren't related. It was just a fond gesture. We didn't have popcorn to feed them, but we picked up some seeds and grain we found on the ground and threw it in the water. The ducks nearly flew to find this delectable meal we had just served them. It was so much fun to watch. They must have been offspring of the former ducks. When we ran out of seeds and things to toss over the bridge, the little ducks seemed to fill of their tasty treat, and they floated ever so gently on the water below. We saw more ducks coming in the distance. I wondered why I had taken a notion to drift down the road, and then I laughed a little inside. I guess I wanted to be that little girl for a few minutes.

Though Joey protested, we walked on back to the cottage. He brightened up when he saw the tire swing moving back and forth. Someone had been there, and it looked like one of our friends from town. Jimmy, Randy, and Felicity loved to come by to visit now and then. They lived closer to the Silica Mill, which was one of the thriving facilities when I was a small child. Mother always called it Sil-ee-key. People worked in shifts and came out covered in white dust. No one knew what the consequences would be until years later when workers began to get very sick from working there.

The Swanson boys were also playing outside. At eight and ten years old respectively, their sister was only six years old. Their mother, Judy Lynne, was a friend from years past. She decided to bring her homemade, secret recipe pound cake. Joey knew he had it made when he saw the boys. He just tolerated their sister. They would swing him or pull him in the wagon until he fell asleep. Of course their sister whined until she was in the wagon too.

Since Judy and the kids were there, we called Phyllis and her new guy friend, Mr. Daniel R. Butler, to come join us. He worked for the post office in Clayton. We were told they were a good match. After all, Phyllis did catch the bridal bouquet at Melissa's wedding two years ago. We knew she would be next. There was lots of room for the children to play outdoors. We ate our most delicious ice cream with the best pound cake too. Then we were all happy and cheery.

Brian and Mitzi told us we would be grandparents in the fall.

Oh my, what a day! I thought, *Grandma, me?*

Mitzi said, "Now Mom, if you don't want to be a grandmama, it's just a little too late."

Without a doubt, I was thrilled beyond words. All I could say was, "Grandma, me, what next?"

David was happy but kept saying, "I'm still working on being a dad, how can I be a grandpa?"

Someone told him that he seemed to have passed that dad test a long time ago and the grandpa and grandma tests were much easier! You'll see, it's easy and you'll have a ball.

We had a surprise when we got home too; our dear Marie and Willie had set their wedding date. She called Mitzi and Brian to ask if they could be wed in the garden just like the two of them. Naturally, you know the answer was yes. They would wait until after their brand new niece or nephew arrived and the newness had worn off. Besides, Mitzi had to be able to fit into a matron of honor dress too.

e⊃

Before we knew it, eight months had passed. David and I drove to Clayton to pick up our Mitzi. She would stay the next couple weeks with us. Brian would drive up if anything happened. Otherwise, Mr. Heater had become pretty dependent on him and would need him until he had to leave.

I walked into the charming rose garden one

more time. It was exceptionally beautiful. It was prettier than I could remember ever seeing it. I felt like my mother was close to me. It seemed as if her presence was strong in the atmosphere.

I pretended she was there and said, "Mom, the new baby is coming. Now I get to be the grand-mama. I could never fill your shoes, nor will I try. Thanks for all the lessons in life and strength you gave to me."

I *thought I heard* a soft, sweet voice answer, "You are welcome, my child. Now go and comfort your own; she needs you. Trisha, look now, the roses are too perfect."

My heart nearly failed me. My knees did. David always kept an eye on me, whether I knew it or not, and he ran out when he saw me falling. He carried me indoors. After he knew I was all right, he spouted off with, "Hey, you're not the one who is supposed to get the attention right now!"

I popped him hard on his arm with my fist and told my daughter what had just happened. Her eyes filled up as she said, "Yes, Mama, it's true; it's time."

"No, honey, it's too early!" I said. I calmed

myself down because I didn't want to scare Mitzi. Then I said, "Well, it must be God's timing or *she* wouldn't be coming so soon." Mitzi agreed. She didn't even fuss about me saying she and not he this time. She was getting a little shaky.

We made the necessary calls and proceeded on our way to Tunis General. Mitzi and Brian rode all cuddled up in the back of the van. She would soon deliver our first grandchild. Aunt Marie was waiting at the emergency room door.

Soon-to-be-Uncle Willie came to the waiting room to be with us. The coffee was either too hot, too strong, or just didn't taste right. I was so anxious just wondering what the baby would look like. What color hair would she have? Yes, I had decided it was a girl. Mitzi and Brian had made the decision to pass on finding out the gender with sonograms. I, for one, loved knowing in my heart that our new little one was a girl.

Marie couldn't be part of the team when they rolled her sister through the big doors for delivery. We all kissed her and told her our prayers were with her. Marie came out of the observation room with a concerned look on her face. She brought

Brian papers to sign. It had to be an emergency C-section. Mitzi was too small to have a seven-pound baby.

I went to the hospital chapel to pray. "Now, Lord, I trust you, and all I can do is put our child and grandbaby in your hands. No other hands are more capable than yours. I thank you, Lord, for your grace and mercy and ask that this baby and mother come through this situation perfect and whole. Amen."

Unbeknown to me, David, Brian, and Willie were right behind me. When I dried my eyes and got up off my knees, they all said amen too. After we had a family group hug, we all thanked God for this blessing.

Twenty minutes later our little girl was born. Our most beautiful Bethany Rose Hughes weighed seven pounds and two ounces and was twenty and a half inches long. Her hair was dark, soft, and curly to boot. David and I were in awe as we witnessed her cry. Then we saw what looked like a smile to us. So perfect. I never knew what a *bundle of joy* really meant until that moment. I thought I did when I had my children, but the love I felt for that grandchild, well, there's just nothing like it.

I can't describe this emotional burst of happiness that flooded over me. Another surprise was the sweet name, Bethany. Mitzi said she loved Mother so and wanted her first daughter to be named after her. Mitzi would heal quickly and bounce back to good health in no time.

Someone said to me one day, "It's the seed of your seed when your grandchild is born." That stuck with me for a reason. All I knew was she was so perfect. Our little rose, Bethany Rose that is.

⁓

More grandchildren came. Mitzi and Brian had two more, Heather Marie and Savannah Kay. Marie and Willie had their wedding in the rose garden later on that same year, and within two years they had the twins, Mandy and Brianne. Willie and Marie were wonderful parents and blessed us with our Carmen Dee three years later. Their last child, Zachary Garrison, was born on October 25, 1998. Now that was our first grandson. Who would have guessed it? Marie and Willie had four children and they were so happy.

It was a good thing our daughters knew about

medicine because our grandchildren sure had their share of bumps and bruises as they ran and played.

 ~

Grandpa and I don't think we have spoiled them too much. David and I are devotedly attached grandparents. We think of all the things we have to do to make sure their childhood has the best of memories. David made sure the sidewalk was just right for roller-skating, but that is sort of out of fashion now the kids told us. We visited Clayton in the springtime of 2003 and went with them to the village park where they performed all their skate-boarding antics. David tried this little strenuous, looking like loads of fun, trick, but wasn't too successful. He slipped I don't know how many times and fell occasionally, but the kids loved it. He had a bump or two but didn't get hurt. All of us laughed and felt this wonderful closeness. I wasn't so adventurous, but I loved watching them.

A BIRD'S-EYE VIEW
of trish's life

What unspeakable joy Trish has now! She could see her reason for existing through her family and God. What wonderful peace that passes all understanding.

It was nice to go home in the fall, feeling good again, as Trish thought of her Mom, Dad, Scarbrough Cottage, and observing the roses most of all. "Winter will be here soon," her mother would say, *"The Roses Are Too Perfect."*

One thing life taught Trish, among many other lessons, is this: *nothing will stay the same. Things will always change.* Accepting those changes is our objective in life. We choose one way or the other. Choices have consequences. When we have hardships, sometimes we will be sad, but we can move on. Oh yes, we'll be angry and upset for a while. There's no denying the pain and misery in our hearts when our loved one has passed on before us, but there is a scripture in the Bible that helps us: "...weeping may endure for a night, but joy cometh in the morning" (Psalm 30:5).

A young woman told me that some would say, "Just snap out of it or get over it!" There are those who feel like they need permission to grieve or cry, but they don't. It takes more time for some than others, but with the Lord's help and guidance, eventually, people gather their inward God-given strength and are able to move forward after the heartache of losing a close loved one. Thank God for his loving grace, and mercy, toward us. Also for, his forgiveness for doubting his Holy Word. He tells us to trust him. "Trust in the LORD with all thine heart; and lean not unto thine own understanding. In all thy ways acknowledge him, and he shall direct thy paths" (Proverbs 3:5–6).